# Clarinet Exam Pieces

## ABRSM Grade 2

Selected from the 2014–2017 syllabus

Name  

Date of exam

## Contents

page

LIST A



Footnotes: Anthony Burton

### Other pieces for Grade 2

LIST A

4 **Diabelli** Ländler. No. 13 from *The Really Easy Clarinet Book*, arr. Davies and Harris (Faber)
5 **Handel** The Harmonious Blacksmith. *Music Through Time for Clarinet*, Book 1, arr. Harris (OUP)
6 **Schubert** Hommage aux belles Viennoises. *Clarinet Basics Repertoire*, arr. Harris (Faber)
7 **Schubert** Ländler (D. 366 No. 6). *Time Pieces for Clarinet*, Vol. 1, arr. Denley (ABRSM)
8 **Trad.** English Country Garden. *Cool Clarinet Repertoire*, Book 2, arr. Hammond (Kevin Mayhew)
9 **Trad. English** Early One Morning *or* The Mermaid. *One More Time! for Clarinet*, arr. Watts (Kevin Mayhew)

LIST B

4 **S. Foster** Serenade: Beautiful Dreamer (*observing repeat*). No. 12 from *First Book of Clarinet Solos*, arr. Davies and Reade (Faber)
5 **Paul Harris** Whiling Away the Time on Those Long Summer Afternoons: from *I Hate Crossing the Break!* (Queen's Temple Publications)
6 **Joplin** I Am Thinking of My Pickaninny Days. *Music Through Time for Clarinet*, Book 1, arr. Harris (OUP)
7 **Christopher Norton** Gloomy: No. 10 from *The Microjazz Clarinet Collection 1* (Boosey & Hawkes)
8 **Weiner** A-B-C. *Time Pieces for Clarinet*, Vol. 1, arr. Denley (ABRSM)
9 **Jeffery Wilson** Dixie: No. 2 from *Jazz Album* (Camden Music)

LIST C

4 **Richard Benger** Bach-Lark: from *30 Tuneful Studies* (Spartan Press)
5 **Demnitz** Study in G. No. 9 from Demnitz, *Elementary School for Clarinet*, p. 5 (Peters) or No. 21 from *80 Graded Studies for Clarinet*, Book 1 (Faber)
6 **Roger Purcell** Hop, Skip and Jump: No. 10 from *Scaling the Heights* (Astute Music)
7 **James Rae** Pieces of Eight *or* Rock Summit: No. 16 *or* No. 19 from *38 More Modern Studies for Solo Clarinet* (Universal)


First published in 2013 by ABRSM (Publishing) Ltd, a wholly owned subsidiary of ABRSM, 24 Portland Place, London W1B 1LU, United Kingdom



Music origination by Julia Bovee
Cover by Kate Benjamin & Andy Potts
Printed in England by Halstan & Co. Ltd, Amersham, Bucks.

# Könnte jeder brave Mann

A:1

from *Die Zauberflöte*, K. 620

Arranged by Brian Hunt, Mavis de Mierre, Michael Illman and Peter Nickol

W. A. Mozart (1756–91)

**Könnte jeder brave Mann (solche Glöckchen finden)** If only every good man could find such little bells
**Die Zauberflöte** The Magic Flute

Wolfgang Amadeus Mozart wrote his last opera, *The Magic Flute*, in the final months of his life for performance at a suburban theatre in the Austrian capital, Vienna. Unlike his operas for the Viennese court, which are in Italian and sung throughout, this opera is in German with spoken dialogue. It is a serious comedy with a pantomime-like plot. At one point in the extended musical finale to Act I, after the cheerful bird-catcher Papageno and the heroine Pamina have been captured by the fierce Monostatos and his slaves, Papageno plays a set of magic bells, which causes their captors to dance off the stage in a docile manner. Pamina and Papageno share a short duet marvelling at this, and at the bells' ability to bring about human harmony. The piece is arranged here with the soprano line of Pamina in the clarinet part.

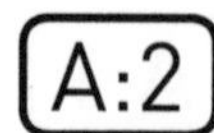


# Lilliburlero

Arranged by Paul Harris

Henry Purcell
(1659–95)

Henry Purcell was the most important English composer of his age, and is often considered one of the greatest of all time. In 1689, 18 of his pieces were included in a collection of keyboard music published in London under the title of *The Second Part of Musick's Hand-maid*. One of them is called 'A New Irish Tune', and is a version of a traditional Irish jig – or possibly an English melody in Irish style – called *Lilliburlero*. The tune was borrowed for use in *The Beggar's Opera*, a successful show in London in 1728, and later acquired various sets of words, including the nursery rhyme 'There was an old woman tossed up in a blanket'. In a slightly different version to Purcell's, the tune became well known internationally through its use as the call sign of BBC World Service radio.

# Deep River

Arranged by Norman Heim

Trad. Spiritual

'Deep River' is a well-known spiritual, a traditional song first sung in the 19th century by slaves in the southern United States. It is familiar to modern concert audiences through its use as the closing number of Sir Michael Tippett's oratorio *A Child of Our Time*, first performed in 1944. The words – which refer to the River Jordan in the Biblical Holy Land, and to the campgrounds of American outdoor church gatherings – express a longing for the peace of death:

> Deep river,
> My home is over Jordan.
> Deep river, Lord,
> I want to cross over into campground.

In this arrangement by the American clarinettist and composer Norman Heim, the written-out repeat (from bar 10) is varied as if by an improvising singer. For the exam, a faster tempo than that indicated by the arranger's metronome mark would be acceptable, to help with breath control: ♩ = *c*.80.

# Shhhh!

No. 1 from *Ten to Go*



Mark Cropton
(born 1961)

Mark Cropton was born in London, studied clarinet and saxophone at Trinity College of Music, and then taught both instruments for 13 years, before emigrating to Australia in 1998. He has written two sets of pieces in varied styles under the title *Ten to Go*, respectively for clarinet and saxophone with piano. The clarinet pieces, published in 2005, concentrate at first on the low chalumeau register. The title of the first, 'Shhhh!', suggests an atmosphere of secrets and stealth.

# Oh, Lady be Good!

B:2

from *Lady, be Good!*

Arranged by John Davies and Paul Harris

Music and lyrics by
George Gershwin (1898–1937)
and Ira Gershwin (1896–1983)

The American composer George Gershwin enjoyed equal success in the concert hall, with jazz-coloured works such as his *Rhapsody in Blue*, and in the theatre, with numerous shows including, towards the end of his short life, the opera *Porgy and Bess*. *Lady, be Good!* was his first full-length collaboration with his lyricist brother Ira, and was one of their most successful musical comedies: it ran for 330 performances in its first run on Broadway in New York in 1924/25, and two years later chalked up almost the same number of performances in the West End of London. The show was named (nearly) after one of its songs which went on to become a standard for jazz singers and players. 'Oh, Lady be Good!' is sung by a devious lawyer named 'Watty' Watkins, who is trying to persuade the penniless Susie to take part in a fraud concerning an inheritance. The chorus (arranged here) starts with the words:

Oh, sweet and lovely lady, be good!
Oh lady, be good to me!

The words 'lady, be good' are set to a phrase featuring lazy crotchet triplets, for example in bars 5 and 7.

# Moderato ma con moto

No. 4 from *Beginners Please!*

Anthony Hedges
(born 1931)

Anthony Hedges studied music at Oxford University, and taught for many years at the University of Hull, in the north-east of England. He has written serious concert music for orchestra, chorus, chamber ensembles and soloists, lighter music for orchestra and many pieces for young players. This is the fourth in a set of eight easy pieces called *Beginners Please!*, originally written for violin and piano, but later arranged by the composer for clarinet and piano. The title of the collection is the traditional call for actors involved in the start of a play to go on stage. The clarinet part should move smoothly between registers.

# Prelude

C:1

from *L'Arlésienne*

Arranged by Peter Lawrance

Georges Bizet
(1838–75)

**L'Arlésienne** The Girl from Arles

The French composer Georges Bizet wrote one of the most popular of all operas, *Carmen*, although it was not well received at its first performance three months before his death, and he did not live to see it become a success. In 1872, he wrote incidental music for a play set in Provence, in the south of France, Alphonse Daudet's *L'Arlésienne*; he also arranged some of the music as a suite for orchestra, which is now a familiar item on concert programmes and recordings. The Prelude to the play, and to the suite, begins with a set of variations on an old Provençal carol, 'March of the Kings', which is first played in unharmonized unison. The melody is presented here for unaccompanied clarinet. For the exam, a tempo of ♩ = *c*.108 would be acceptable.

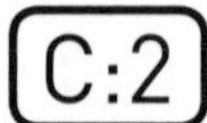


It is **illegal** to make unauthorized copies of this copyright music.

# Study in C

No. 1 from 'Die gebräuchlichsten dynamischen Bezeichnungen'
from *Elementarschule für Klarinette*

Friedrich Demnitz
(1845–90)

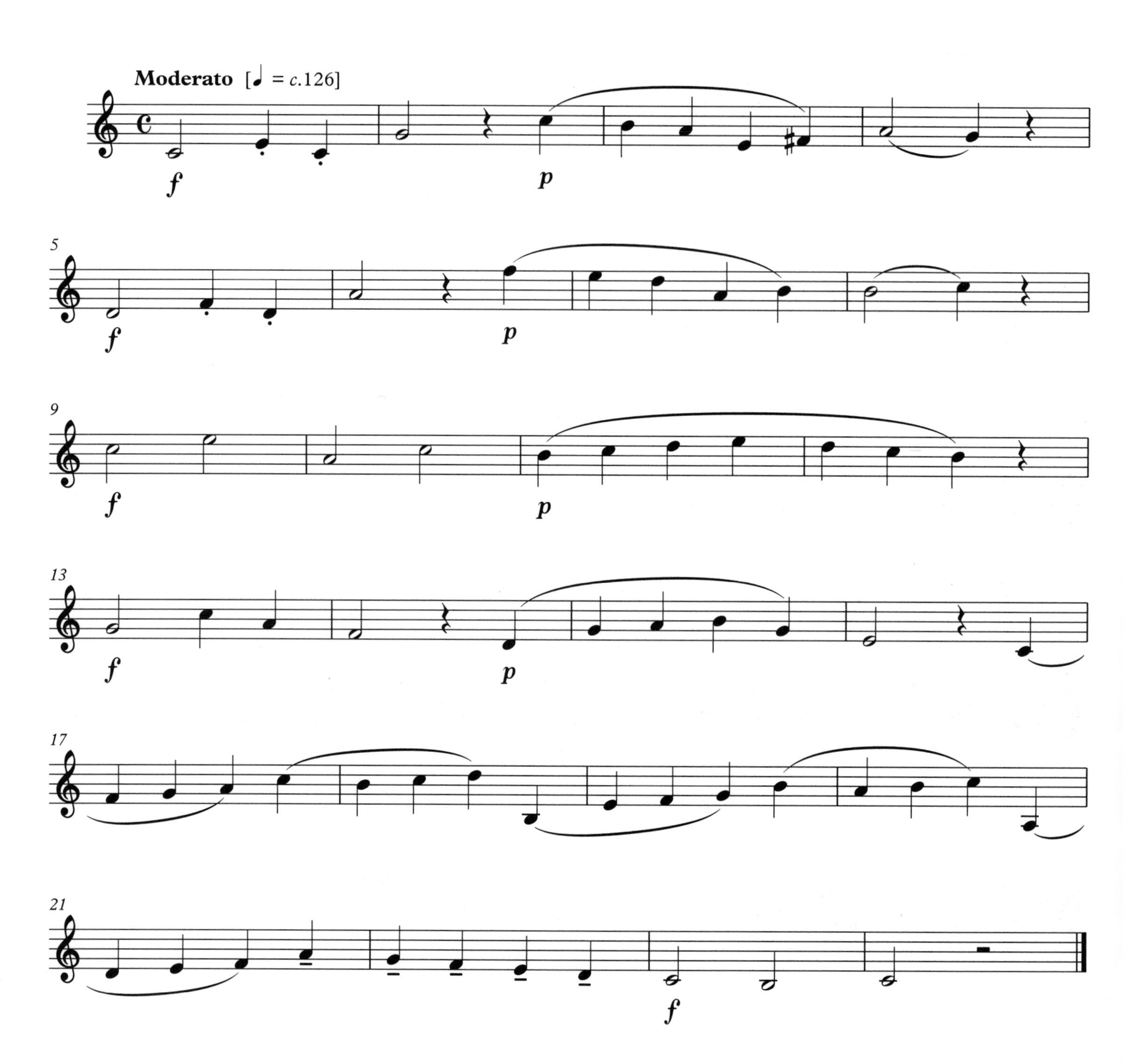


**Die gebräuchlichsten dynamischen Bezeichnungen** The most common dynamic markings
**Elementarschule für Klarinette** Elementary School for Clarinet

Friedrich Demnitz was principal clarinettist of the court orchestra, now known as the Staatskapelle, in the German city of Dresden, and a teacher at the conservatoire there. His *Elementary School for Clarinet,* still in print today, includes studies designed to develop tone production. This is the first study in a section devoted to 'The most common dynamic markings': the study alternates not only between loud and soft, but also between detached and smooth articulation.
Source: *Elementarschule für Klarinette* (Peters, n.d.)

# Skedaddle

C:3

from *Cool School for Clarinet*

Chris Gumbley studied clarinet, piano and composition at the Huddersfield School of Music in the north of England, but now lives in his native West Midlands. He teaches saxophone, clarinet and jazz piano, performs in classical and jazz groups including his own quintet, runs a jazz club called Gumbles, and has his own publishing company. His *Cool School for Clarinet* is a collection of jazz-based pieces. The eighth number is called 'Skedaddle', a slang word meaning 'make a quick getaway'. It is a study in jazz rhythms, to be played with swung quavers, including rests and dotted notes: the composer suggests thinking of the rhythm ♩♪ ♩♪ ♩♪ ♩♪ (triplets) as a template, and ensuring all the notes fit into that pattern.